CW00701635

WOULD
YOU
RATHER?

WOULD YOU RATHER?

Harrison Brocklehurst

WELBECK

Published by Welbeck
An imprint of Welbeck Non-Fiction Limited,
part of Welbeck Publishing Group.
Based in London and Sydney
www.welbeckpublishing.com

First published by Welbeck in 2022

A CIP catalogue record for this book is available
from the British Library

ISBN
Hardback – 9781802793406
eBook – 9781802793413

Typeset by seagulls.net
Printed and bound in the UK

10 9 8 7 6 5 4 3 2 1

My Grandma would perhaps turn in her grave if I dedicated a book this gross to her. So this is for Reggie, our forever puppy, whose fur was almost as orange as the cover of this book and who lived his short life as silly as every word in it. We miss you always.

CONTENTS

CONTENTS

INTRODUCTION

Life is full of tough decisions. So what's a better way to fill your downtime than a book full of more? Hundreds more, in fact. If tearing your brain out with horrors you'd never want to consider is your idea of a relaxing pastime, then read on. The ironic thing about Would You Rather is that none of us would rather. We'd choose neither, and then hope we never have to think on it again. With this book, you do not have the privilege of neither. Make your choice, and choose between the rock and the hard place. Nobody will judge you for it. Much.

FOOD
AND
DRINK

I really hope you're hungry. It wouldn't be any fun putting you off whatever meal you eat next if you weren't.

Would you rather spunk mayo or piss ketchup?

Would you rather have Maltesers for eyes or chocolate buttons for nails?

Would you rather only eat
Rustlers burgers for the rest
of your life or eat 50 spiders
of varying size in one
harrowing sitting?

*Would you rather smash up one
of your fingers with a hammer or
have to eat roast dinners without
gravy for the rest of time?*

Would you rather drown in a sea of paperclips or burn in a vat of molten soup?

Would you rather be hungover and have to eat a pizza made of cardboard or be hangry and have to eat a Chinese takeaway that tasted like soil?

Would you rather lick the pipes of the McDonald's ice cream machine or lick the grease from the Burger King patty grill?

Would you rather eat out-of-date chocolate off someone's beer belly or eat nice chocolate off a cow's filthy udder?

Would you rather drink ten pints of water from a kids swimming pool or one teacup from ten different people's bath water?

Would you rather everything you eat for the rest of your life taste like pork or taste like Percy Pigs?

Would you rather drink piss-flavoured Lucozade or drink someone's piss and it tasted like Lucozade?

Would you rather eat the same meal forever or never be allowed to watch Netflix again?

For the rest of your life, would you rather only be able to eat McDonald's cheese or only be allowed to use Domino's garlic & herb dip as your only sauce for food (including gravy on roast dinners)?

Would you rather have to eat two buckets of sand or drink 12 buckets of sea water?

Would you rather only be able to eat wilted lettuce or only be able to drink pitifully weak cordial?

Would you rather have to replace grated cheese with pubes when you put it on your meals or have grated cheese for pubes?

Would you rather only be able to drink straight sambuca or straight tequila for the rest of your life?

Would you rather have to pour beer on your cereal or Coca Cola on your curries?

Would you rather have to use caramel instead of ketchup or ketchup instead of caramel?

Would you rather eat a rabbit poo muffin or a snail slime croissant?

Would you rather eat a hair sandwich or a fingernail wrap?

*Would you rather any crisps
you eat for the rest of your life
be soggy or any water you
drink going forward to
be room temperature?*

Would you rather be forced
to eat five blocks of mouldy
cheese or down one bottle
of gone-off milk?

Would you rather all
your food smelled like fish
or everything you ate
tasted like fish?

*Would you rather all Mini Eggs
you eat be spider's eggs or all
candy floss be spider's web?*

Would you rather every piece of toast you make be burnt or every pizza you eat still have dough that's raw in the middle?

Would you rather have to brush your teeth with full-fat Coke or never be able to eat any vegetables ever again?

Would you rather have to shit out a Subway footlong or throw up 20 McDonald's nuggets?

Would you rather never be able to order your favourite takeaway again or never be able to watch porn again?

Would you rather have free Nando's for the rest of your life or have the best orgasm on earth once a year?

Would you rather sit in a hot tub filled with casserole for ten hours or drink ten bottles of vinegar as fast as you can?

Would you rather have
dusty Dorito fingers all the
time or never be able to wash
your hands after having a
sticky orange?

Would you rather have to eat a burger that you know has saliva in it or finish off a rotten apple?

*Would you rather never eat meat
again or have to personally kill
the animal every time you
want to eat that meat?*

Would you rather only eat
porridge for the rest of your
life or have to eat only dog
food for a year?

Would you rather only be able to eat bananas or have every food you taste be unbearably spicy?

Would you rather only be able to drink lukewarm tea or boiling hot coffee?

POLITICS

Take comfort in the fact that, whatever lies ahead in the chapter to come, it can't be any worse than the current state of Parliament.

Would you rather be stuck in a lift for 18 and a half hours with Ann Widdecombe or Priti Patel?

Would you rather spend a year spoon-feeding Donald Trump or a day wiping Nigel Farage's arse?

Would you rather take medical advice from Donald Trump or Yahoo answers?

Would you rather take
Stalin for a McDonald's or
take Margaret Thatcher
for a KFC?

Would you rather have a room
in your house wallpapered
with portraits of the Queen or
have a giant framed picture
of Keir Starmer over
your fireplace?

Would you rather be a Tory
in a family of Corbyn fans
or a lefty in a family of
Thatcherites?

*Would you rather jump into
a lake of alligators or call
Vladimir Putin a stupid
twat to his face?*

Would you rather have to spend a day in a room with the thing that scares you the most or have a touchy-feely date with David Cameron?

Would you rather have to read all of Nadine Dorries' terribly reviewed novels from start to finish or go on a week's holiday to Ibiza with Jacob Rees-Mogg?

Would you rather have a bad hairline and not be allowed to go bald or have to wash Boris Johnson's underwear every day, by hand, for the rest of your life?

CELEBS, TELLY AND MUSIC

Chock full of
nuisances, menaces
and egomaniacs.

Whose Christmas album would you rather be forced to listen to on loop every December for the rest of your life: Robbie Williams or Gary Barlow?

Would you rather drive around America in a van with James Corden or go on an Arctic expedition with Jonathan Ross?

Would you rather watch Ant and Dec fisting each other or watch Mel and Sue recreate 2 Girls 1 Cup?

Would you rather have the power to stop COVID-19 from happening or undo the existence of Olly Murs?

Would you rather climb a mountain with Dick and Dom or deep sea dive with Holly and Phil?

Would you rather have to watch every film in the Marvel Cinematic Universe and tell everyone you think it's the peak of cinema or take your chances of survival in the *Saw* franchise?

Would you rather have to laugh at every single joke when you watch *Friends* or spend an hour watching *The Big Bang Theory*?

Would you rather have no teeth or have the name "Coleen Nolan" tattooed across your neck?

Would you rather do ten years in a Tudor England prison or ten years in a car with Rebekah Vardy?

Would you rather have to enthusiastically watch 200 episodes of *Songs of Praise* or hand clean the sticky floors of 30 cinemas?

Would you rather go out,
find a pig, kill it, butcher it
for its meat and then dispose
of the carcass or have Jessie J
scream in your ear for
an hour straight?

*Would you rather someone
walk in on you naked and you
can't cover up or someone
walk in on you listening to
Gary Glitter's music?*

Would you rather have a soggy bottom on *Bake Off* or go on *Four in a Bed* and forget to dust your hotel's rooms?

Would you rather inadvertently destroy the entirety of Glastonbury festival with a fire you caused or have to go and camp at Leeds Fest with a load of teenagers every year?

Would you rather spend a year in a log cabin with Laurence Llewelyn-Bowen or spend a year rowing across the Atlantic with Adrian Chiles?

Would you rather spend five months as Kanye West's publicist or work in Boris Johnson's cabinet?

Would you rather go on
I'm A Celeb and be voted to do
all the Bushtucker Trials or
have to spend a month in a
luxury Bahamas resort
with Piers Morgan?

*Would you rather flash the Queen
repeatedly or have to watch the*
Fifty Shades of Grey *trilogy
with Camilla Parker-Bowles as
she tells you about her sex life
with Prince Charles?*

Would you rather have snot on your face that you can never get rid of or have to spend the rest of your life watching Adam Sandler films back to back?

Would you rather be personally responsible for somehow deleting Spotify for the entire world or be caught with a dangerous weapon inside Buckingham Palace?

Would you rather be forced to watch every episode of *How I Met Your Mother* in one painfully long sitting or only be able to watch the news on TV for the rest of your life?

Would you rather spend ten hours watching paint dry or listening to Torvill and Dean go on about the Bolero?

*Would you rather make a
massive mistake in Gordon
Ramsay's restaurant and suffer
the consequences or have to
spend a day in the company
of Jamie Oliver discussing
turkey twizzlers?*

Would you rather be stuck in a
burning building or stuck
on the boat from *Jaws?*

Would you rather never be allowed to go to the cinema again or every time you go people around you are talking through the film?

Would you rather never get to watch films again or never get to listen to music again?

Would you rather be smacked on the bum with Thor's hammer or give Thanos' ear a wet willy and suffer the consequences?

Would you rather have to face off against The Bride from *Kill Bill* or Michael Myers from *Halloween*?

Would you rather give a blowjob to Hercules or Hades?

Would you rather be stuck in Westview from *WandaVision* forever or have to watch Jared Leto act dreadfully in *Morbius* for all of time?

Would you rather be the person to forbid all children from watching *Encanto* and become a global enemy or be revealed as the person who forced the Spice Girls to disband?

Who would you rather go up against in a fist fight to the death: Dwayne 'The Rock' Johnson or Buffy the Vampire Slayer?

Would you rather go on a disappointing date with Leonardo Di Caprio or have a bang average snog with Robert Pattinson?

Which song would you rather listen to on a draining loop for the rest of your life: "Dance Monkey" by Tones & I or "Happy" by Pharrell?

Would you rather spend a year in a recording studio with a chaotic and unpredictable Ozzy Osbourne or an unmotivated, writer's-block-suffering Adele?

Would you rather try to launch a pop career for Laurence Fox or be responsible for the musical comeback of *Crazy Frog*?

SEX

Now would be the
perfect time to start
clutching your pearls.

Would you rather receive 50 spanks or dish out 250 spanks?

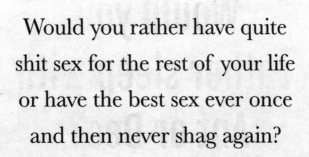

Would you rather have quite shit sex for the rest of your life or have the best sex ever once and then never shag again?

Would you rather be a multimillionaire and never have sex again or shag your ultimate crush right this second but never earn more than 20k a year?

Would you rather sleep with Ant or Dec?

Would you rather give up oral sex or pizza for the rest of your life?

Would you rather never masturbate again or never kiss again?

Would you rather your genitals always smelled or that the genitals of everyone you have sex with smelled?

Would you rather your face go green every time you think about sex or emit a high pitched scream every time you think about food?

Would you rather be able
to have multiple orgasms
whenever you want but it's
always within earshot of your
parents or only be able to have
one orgasm a month but
it's amazing?

Would you rather post a
video of you masturbating to
TikTok and have it all over
the 'For You' page or send
one to all of your friends
on Facebook?

*Would you rather be in debt for
the rest of your life or shag the
love of your life now and then
never see them again?*

Would you rather feel uncontrollably horny at every inappropriate time for the rest of your life or feel cripplingly embarrassed every time you speak to someone?

Would you rather cum every hour, on the hour, or accidentally chomp down on your tongue every 30 minutes?

Would you rather someone catch you masturbating in church or stealing from a disabled person?

Would you rather get trapped in a lift with the second to last person you shagged or get trapped in a lift with the last person your ex shagged?

Would you rather never be able to snog someone in a club again or have to play Wordle every day but never get the word correct?

Would you rather have everyone you sleep with think you're amazing in bed but you don't enjoy it or have everyone think you're shit in bed but it feels amazing for you?

Would you rather be made to suck 500 random toes or lick ten random bumholes?

Would you rather have to count every tissue you've ever used to clean up semen or have to watch back footage of every sexual encounter you've ever had?

BODILY FLUIDS AND OTHER VILE HORRORS

Sighs. I'm so sorry for putting you through this.

Would you rather have permanent diarrhoea or shit out a bowling ball once a year?

Would you rather someone burp ten times into your mouth or someone do one big, vile fart in your mouth?

Would you rather squirt BBQ sauce from your hands every time you farted or sweat mango chutney every time you burp?

Would you rather have to walk to the shop with semen on your face or go into work with semen all over your clothing?

Would you rather sit in a bath of blood or shower under raining sick?

Would you rather go to someone's party and piss the bed or come home from a party and find that someone's pissed your bed?

Would you rather piss vinegar or sneeze chilli sauce?

Would you rather eat a sample of five random people's shit or have to taste test all the different vomit you've ever thrown up in your life?

Would you rather a truly evil person be born every time you poo or have someone die every time you yawn?

Would you rather cry Nutella or sweat jam?

Would you rather never be able to wipe your arse or never be able to wash your armpits (and unable to wear deodorant)?

Would you rather be caught scratching your genitals and having a sniff or get caught smelling your own fart and enjoying it?

Would you rather drink unflushed toilet bowl water or clean a restaurant's kitchen with your tongue?

Would you rather be sick every time you go on your phone or piss yourself every time you eat?

Would you rather shit yourself every time you have a bath or do a massive poo in every swimming pool you ever swim in?

Would you rather have to swim in a pit of cum for two hours or a pit of shit for ten minutes?

Would you rather have to eat 30 bogies from someone else's nose or one ice cube of your own frozen shit?

Would you rather shart yourself every time you cough or lose a year of your life every time you stub your toe?

Would you rather spit in someone's face every time you speak loudly or fart whenever you enter a room?

Would you rather piss yourself whenever you go to the hairdresser's or vomit in your dentist's face every time they check your teeth?

Would you rather have a stranger shit in every room of your house or shit in one room of a stranger's house and be outed for it at a dinner party?

Would you rather eat a
teaspoon of someone else's
earwax or drink a shot of pus?

*Would you rather piss the bed
whenever you cough or spill
a red drink down your top
every time you think about
the weather?*

Would you rather sit in a basin of a stranger's piss or a close friend's semen?

Would you rather sleep on a bed made of earwax or have to sit on a sofa made of pubes every night?

FAMILY

Ahh, a wholesome chapter of respite! I'm only kidding. These are vile.

Would you rather watch your parents have sex every day for the rest of your life or join in once?

Would you rather be responsible for losing your mate's phone and keys on a night out or spill a bottle of red wine on your mum's cream sofa?

Would you rather have to try and explain memes to a Victorian child or try and teach the oldest person in your family how to make a complicated TikTok?

Would you rather drink your gran's piss or eat Lady Gaga's chemically preserved meat dress that may or may not have also been pissed on?

Would you rather post a full frontal nude photo to your Instagram or send a sex tape to your mum?

Would you rather listen to your grandma have sex or have to show her your porn history?

Would you rather send a no-context picture of your genitals to your mum or to your dad?

Would you rather plan your sister's 21st and she hate it or volunteer to host Christmas for the whole family and every single thing go wrong and ruin the entire day for everyone?

Would you rather never get to see your siblings again or never get to see your favourite pet again?

Would you rather lose your mum's wedding ring or be personally responsible for sinking a boat?

Would you rather your parents watch you do drugs or go to a very sad funeral off your tits on MDMA and have to act natural?

Would you rather show your parents the messages you've sent on dating apps or have your ugliest nude go up on a billboard in Times Square for 60 seconds?

Would you rather the police catch you with a LOT of drugs or your grandparents catch you shagging in their bed?

ANIMALS

Don't call PETA on me,
I beg.

Would you rather never get to own a pet again or be the owner of an embarrassingly ugly and mortifyingly untrained dog?

Would you rather have the teeth of a boar or the penis of a dog?

Would you rather be able to speak to animals and nobody believe you about it or con the world into thinking you can speak to animals, get fame and fortune, but you have to murder a few puppies in the process?

Would you rather be eaten by a snake or devoured by a shoal of piranhas?

Would you rather be painlessly crawled on by 500 spiders or get stung by 20 bees?

Would you rather be a fish
with the brain of a human
or a human with the
brain of a fish?

Would you rather your leg be nibbled on by a big furry animal or nibbled on by a big human with a furry kink?

Would you rather only be able to communicate in barks or meows?

Would you rather have to eat ten slugs or have to squish 500 slugs to death with your bare feet?

Would you rather be eaten by ants or by a person?

Would you rather wet yourself every time you saw a cat or shit yourself every time you saw a dog?

Would you rather punch a fish to death (à la Neil on *The Inbetweeners*) or have fish angrily try to slap you to death with their tails?

Would you rather every chip you ate be cold or every cat you met hate you with a fiery passion?

Would you rather have 20 wet and alive fish drop on you every time you get into bed or have to do 20 shots of vodka every time you wake up in the morning?

Would you rather an octopus be in your bathroom every time you need the toilet or have to sneak past an angry wolf every time you leave your house?

Would you rather be someone's pet guinea pig or be a monkey in a safari park?

Would you rather have to sleep in a bed of dog hair every night or have all your soft furnishings be made of chicken feathers?

Would you rather have to fight a furious sheep or sit on a hedgehog?

*Would you rather jump in
the hyena enclosure at the zoo
or be made to lie down in
the scorpion exhibit?*

Would you rather be a deer
with no legs that everyone
pities or be a massive fly
that horrifies everyone?

Would you rather be a mosquito or a slug?

Would you rather the spend the next year of your life in prison after being falsely convicted for murder or live the next year of your life as a pigeon?

Would you rather smell
like fox poo or a cat's
soiled litter box?

*Would you rather live in a world
where angry sharks have grown
legs and roam the streets or a
world where vicious snakes have
worked out how to fly and
attack from above?*

WORK

Agonising over these is NOT a valid excuse for calling in sick, I'm afraid.

Would you rather send a picture of your gaping arsehole to your parents or your boss?

Would you rather wake up every 20 minutes when you're trying to sleep or have to do an additional four hours every working day?

Would you rather have sex
on your boss's desk once and
get arrested for it or have your
phone drain down to 10%
battery every time you
looked at it?

Would you rather lose your
job tomorrow or not be allowed
in a single pub for the
next two years?

Would you rather spend a
day (9am to 5pm) in the office
with an angry bear rampaging
through it or single handedly
have to clean the office
kitchen for the rest of time?

*Would you rather have to lick
a club dance floor ten times
or lick the toilet bowl in
your workplace once?*

Would you rather never get promoted or never get a payrise?

Would you rather get your dream job with the worst boss imaginable or have an average job with the best manager and team?

Would you rather be caught shagging in the lift at work or punch your boss in the face and try and blag it as an accident?

Would you rather make a huge mistake at work and everyone know it was you or have to fire your best mate in the office and have them hate you forever?

Would you rather get fired for something you didn't do or frame a colleague for your own mistake and watch as they get fired?

Would you rather make
a tit of yourself at the
work Christmas party or
accidentally destroy your hotel
room on a business trip?

*Would you rather hate your life
at work but be really rich or love
your life at work and scrape by?*

Would you rather fall off your office chair in front of everyone or spill soup on the work cleaner?

Would you rather be screamed at while working a till in retail or be yelled at by an evil chef while working as a waiter?

TOUGH CALLS

This chapter is a jumble
sale of the hardest
decisions you'll ever
make. Erm... enjoy!

Would you rather suddenly lose one of your arms or only be able to watch *Mrs. Brown's Boys* for the rest of your life?

Would you rather have to pull off all your nails yourself or have someone else pull out all your hair?

Would you rather stub your toe 200 times or get 200 papercuts?

Would you rather re-live your final year of school with your memories now or live now with the mindset of how you were in your final year of school?

Would you rather punch a baby in the face or push an old woman with a walking stick to the floor… and then punch *her* in the face?

Would you rather lick a London Underground tube seat or a Wetherspoon's carpet?

Would you rather never be able to thank someone when they hold the door open for you or never be able to put the Next Customer sign on a supermarket till's conveyer belt ever again?

Would you rather have Covid for Christmas or go to four consecutive "gender reveal" parties and have to be enthusiastic at each?

Would you rather spend an isolated month alone in a disused mine shaft or live your entire life (including any and all holidays) in Skegness?

Would you rather mock Henry VIII's chin-beard to his face or try your luck in a zombie apocalypse?

Would you rather get the plague in 1346 or watch the film *Cats* (2019) on constant loop for a year?

Would you rather be sick on the coffin at a funeral or be forced to piss on a bride at her wedding?

Would you rather make a really shit and pretty offensive film with your name plastered all over it or make the best film ever made and have to see someone else take all the credit and glory for it?

Would you rather have a permanently sandy arse crack or have a stone in your shoe that you can never take out?

Would you rather wake up in the middle of being cremated or wake up having been buried alive?

Would you rather spend a week living in the sheer hell that is London Euston station or one night sleeping in a sewer?

Would you rather lick one gangrenous foot or lick under every chewing-gum-covered table in your secondary school?

Would you rather run for a bus in front of loads of people and miss it or run for the Tube, get on it but get trapped in the doors and cause a scene?

Would you rather lose all the money in your bank account right now or go on 50 dates with your ex?

Would you rather have sandpaper for toilet roll or only be allowed to brush your teeth with syrup?

Would you rather give up WiFi or brushing your teeth for a month?

Would you rather never see colour again or never be able to tell genres of music apart?

Would you rather lose the ability to lie or to tell the truth?

Would you rather sneeze unstoppably for a day and draw loads of attention to yourself or fart silently and constantly for a week?

Would you rather have to dress in a suit every time you go to the shop for food or have to dress in your worst and scruffiest clothes for every wedding and funeral?

Would you rather lose your memories of the last ten years or lose the next ten years of your life?

Would you rather be embarrassingly drunk and have to be put to bed after every night out for the rest of time, or have to be the one who looks after the embarrassingly drunk person?

Would you rather be three hours early or 45 minutes late for everything for the rest of your life?

Would you rather have a permanently filthy kitchen or a permanently filthy bathroom?

Would you rather go to prison for 5 years or lose 15 years of your life to a coma?

Would you rather never be hugged again or have to hug the smelliest person on the planet three times a day?

Would you rather never go on holiday again or every time you go on holiday you lose a body part?

Would you rather show your partner your porn history or show your old teacher your most-watched video (in full)?

Would you rather never be able to use a dating app again or only match with people who don't fancy you?

Would you rather be extremely rich for the next ten years then go bankrupt, or live like you live now forever without getting any richer?

Would you rather get to spend an hour in the past and solve an unsolved mystery for the present, or get to spend a week in the future and witness something huge but not get to tell anyone?

Would you rather be a really loud eater or have the worst laugh ever?

Would you rather live the rest of your life as a nun or live knowing you're absolutely going to burn in hell upon your death?

Would you rather have your last ten lies exposed to the world or slap an old woman hard across the face with a pan?

Would you rather never have access to YouTube again or be able to keep your YouTube access on the condition that you post an embarrassing Facebook status every day?

Would you rather do a year in a maximum security prison or live the rest of your life in a luxury villa but you're never allowed to leave it?

Would you rather know how rich you're going to be for the rest of your life or know how your body's going to look when you're 40 years older?

Would you rather lose a limb or have to say yes to someone trying to recruit you as a forex trader on Instagram?

Would you rather have a permanently clogged toilet or only be able to take your bins out once a year?

Would you rather see every text your partner has sent during your relationship or find out who Jack the Ripper actually was?

Would you rather only be able to communicate in three words of your choosing or only be able to see three colours of your choice?

Would you rather fall to the floor every ten steps you take or have to remove an item of clothing every time you need a drink?

Would you rather be stuck in a plane toilet with no toilet roll or stuck in a National Express toilet for the entire duration of a 16 hour coach journey?

Would you rather have
permanently itchy eyeballs
or permanently itchy feet?

*Would you rather have no clean
underwear for the rest of your
life or whenever you come home
realise that someone's stolen
all your lightbulbs?*

Would you rather have wet feet squelching in your shoes that you can never dry or have to dry yourself with a rancid, dirty towel for the rest of time?

Would you rather be kicked in the genitals every time you had a runny nose or lose ten quid every time you ate an apple?

Would you rather only be able to communicate in sniffs or yawns?

Would you rather have to go on live TV and sing but not know the words or have to give a guided tour of the Tower of London to 500 paying tourists and not know a single fact?

Would you rather never be able to apologise for bumping into a stranger or never be able to thank a server when they take your plates?

Would you rather permanently smell musty or look sweaty all the time?

Would you rather always be dizzy or always be furiously angry?

Would you rather smack someone round the face every time you yawned or have to run 1000 metres every time you ate a biscuit?

Would you rather have an intense sex dream about someone you never want to have a sex dream about every time you sleep or have nothing but nightmares again for the rest of your life?

Would you rather never be able to wear a coat again or have to wear a coat at all times, including during the scorching heat?

Would you rather fart at hot yoga and everyone know or fall over in the middle of a pose and cause the whole class to tumble down with you?

Would you rather lose the
World Cup for England once
or have to go and watch
professional snooker twice
a week forever?

Would you rather never have to wipe your arse again or never catch a cold again?

BODY CHANGES

Have body image issues?
You will after this
hellish array.

Would you rather have tits for hands or butt cheeks for feet?

Would you rather one of your arse cheeks be huge or one deflated and saggy?

Would you rather bathe in mud forever or only be allowed to use Lynx Africa as your deodorant AND fragrance?

Would you rather have purple legs or green arms?

*Would you rather have
ham shanks for hands or
battered cod for feet?*

Would you rather have a penis
that was made of paper or
one made of metal?

Would you rather have accordions for legs or trumpets for arms?

Would you rather replace all your moles with little eyes or with little toes?

Would you rather have a
nose for a bumhole or a
bumhole for a nose?

Would you rather have legs the length of toenails or toenails the length of your legs?

Would you rather have a
penis the length of your toes
or toes all the same length
as your penis?

Would you rather have a face
that looks like an arsehole or
an arse that looks like a face?

Would you rather feel like you have the most gorgeous face on earth but everyone thinks you're ugly or have the ugliest face on earth and everyone think you're beautiful?

Would you rather have straws for fingers or pasta for hair?

Would you rather look 80 from the chest up or 80 from the chest down?

Would you rather have pubes
made of needles or eyelashes
made of razors?

Would you rather have finger-length legs or leg-length fingers?

Would you rather be gorgeous with no teeth or look how you look now with the ugliest teeth ever?

Would you rather have the face of a dog or have cow udders between your legs?

Would you rather your nipples grow every time you lied or your fingernails shrink every time you showered?

Would you rather have arse holes for nipples or clitori for fingers?

Would you rather have skin made of glass or hair made of tissue paper?

Would you rather have tits down to the floor that you can't get a reduction on or legs half the size of the ones you have now?

Would you rather have cats for hands or dogs for feet?

Would you rather have dirty fingernails at all times or have a love bite on your neck that never goes away?

Would you rather have permanently sweaty genitals or always have bad breath?

Would you rather be completely hairless and nothing ever grow back or be covered head to toe in hair and be unable to trim any off?